End of term!

Keith Gaines

Nelson

It was the last week of term at Waterloo School.
It was the last week that the children would be in
Mr Belter's class.

On Thursday, Mr Belter said to the children,
'Tomorrow we will have an end of term party, but
today I have lots of work for you to do.'

'Oh, Mr Belter,' said Tony.
'It's the end of the last week of term.
We don't have to work today, do we?'
'It's never too late to start, Tony,' said Mr Belter.

Mr Belter gave everyone a paper.
At the top of the paper, it said,
'*What do you know about Wellington Square*?'
'What's this for?' said Jamila.
'We are going to find out who knows all about
Wellington Square and about the things that have
happened to the people who live in it,' said Mr Belter.
'Put your name at the top of the paper, and then
you can have a go at the first one.'

What do you know about Wellington Square?
You can take part in this!
You need a paper with 1 to 20 down the left-hand side.
When you have finished, you can find out if you
were right.

4

'Here's the first one,' said Mr Belter.
'Number 1.
Rocky told us about the fox that lives under the shed in his back garden.
He told us about how the fox was stealing food, and how Mr Crisp tried to trap it in a box with a flap on.
What I want to know is:
What sort of food was the fox stealing from the fish and chip shop?'

'Number 2,' said Mr Belter.
'Ben can swim well now, but can you remember
when he couldn't swim?
Ben told us about the time that he fell into the canal.
What sort of animal did Ben rescue from the canal?'

'Number 3,' said Mr Belter.
'We have heard quite a lot about Brian, the
chimp who lives with Mr Keeping.
Mr Keeping brought him into school once for us to see.
Mr Keeping told us about his favourite food.
There are two things Brian loves to eat. What are they?'

'Number 4,' said Mr Belter.
'Tony and Tessa brought their masks into school.
They told us about how they frightened Mrs Nash when
they knocked on her door.
They had bought the masks from a
shop in Wellington Square.
Who owns the shop where Tony and Tessa
bought their masks?'

'Number 5,' said Mr Belter.
'Jamila told us all about when she went to
the fair with Rocky and Ben.
She told us about how she found that
little white dog, playing with a stick.
Can you remember who owned the little dog?'

'Number 6,' said Mr Belter.
'Rocky told me that he telephoned the
police, believing that he had found a bomb.
He found a box on a bench in the park, and
he thought it looked like a bomb.'
Suddenly, Kevin got up, pointing at Rocky.
'So it was you who told the police it was a bomb!
I've been trying to find out who it was for ages.
I'd only left it on the bench for a minute.
You should have kept your nose out of my box.
You shouldn't have touched my...'
'Sit down, Kevin,' shouted Mr Belter.
'I don't want any trouble.'
'Oh, I don't really mind,' said Kevin.
'Now I've got a lovely new...'
'Don't tell us, Kevin,' said Mr Belter.
'I want to know:
What did the bomb turn out to be?'

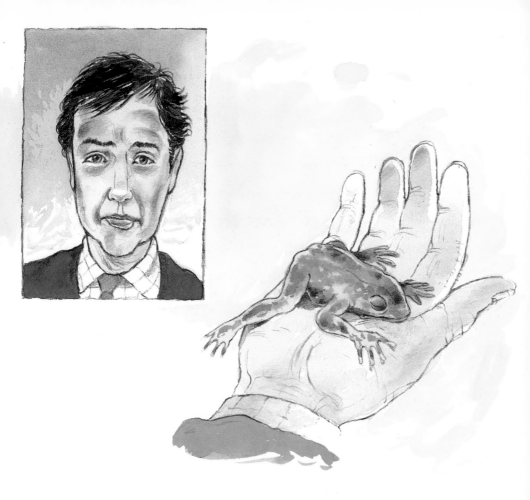

'Number 7,' said Mr Belter.

'Tony and Tessa and Mr Keeping found that someone
had been putting rubbish into the pond in the park.
When Tessa told us all about it, she said that
they had found a dead frog.
It had been killed by something that had
been put into the pond.
What had killed the animals in the pond?'

'Number 8,' said Mr Belter.
'We've been on one or two school trips together.
Do you remember when we went on a
school trip to the castle?'
'I remember that,' said Ben.
'I remember how Rocky and I got
locked in the dungeon.
It was horrible – it was like a bad dream!'
'What I want to know is,' said Mr Belter,
'what is the name for the water which
goes all round the castle?'

'Number 9,' said Mr Belter.
'We had a break-in at the school.
PC Kent told me how Kevin helped the
police to catch the burglar.
The burglar had broken a window and
got into this classroom.
The burglar took something.
What did the burglar steal from the school?'

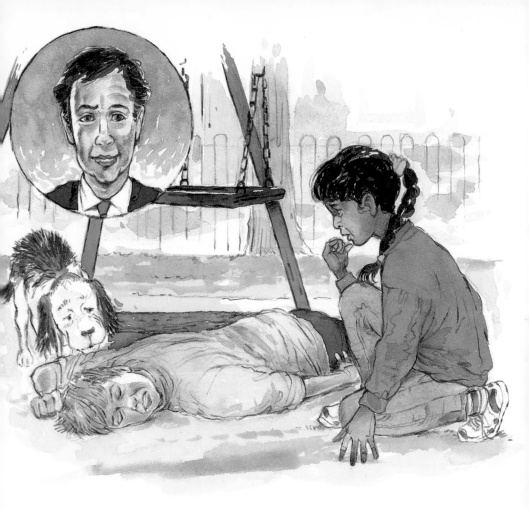

'Number 10,' said Mr Belter.
'Rocky, can you remember when you fell off the swing?'
'No,' said Rocky. 'I can't remember anything about
it until I woke up in hospital.'
'Well,' said Mr Belter.
'Jamila told me about what happened and
we talked about it in school, but
can you remember who called an ambulance?'

'Number 11,' said Mr Belter.
'When we had the cross-country race,
Ben stopped to help Kevin.
They were very slow to get back, because
Kevin had hurt his foot.'
'Yes,' said Ben. 'I hoped to win that race.'
'Well,' said Mr Belter, 'Ben didn't win the race itself,
but because Ben was a really good sport,
he won something much better.
Mr March gave him something.
What object did Mr March give Ben?'

'Number 12,' said Mr Belter.

'Wing Chan told me about when he got his kite stuck in a tree and Rocky climbed up to get it.'

'Yes,' said Rocky.

'I thought I could just knock it down, but I got stuck. I remember that I wished I'd listened to Fred and not climbed all the way up the tree.'

'Someone got a ladder,' said Mr Belter.

'Someone climbed up the ladder and got Rocky and the kite down.

Who got Rocky and the kite down from the tree?'

'Number 13,' said Mr Belter.

'Rocky and Fred were a bit surprised at finding an
old bomb when they were having a dig in Fred's roses.
Do you remember how lots of policemen
came and moved everyone into the
school until the bomb was defused?
After the bomb was taken away, Fred came into
school and told us about what life was like in
Wellington Square in the war, when he was a boy.
He told us about his Grandad and the work he did.
What was Fred's Grandad's work in the war?'

'Number 14,' said Mr Belter.
'I'm still talking about the old bomb that
Fred and Rocky found.
After a man from the army came to defuse the bomb,
Fred gave Rocky a special present.
I want to know what the present was.
It's an easy one for Rocky, but you should
all know, because Rocky brought it in to show us.
So, what did Fred give Rocky to remember
the day he found a bomb?'

'Number 15,' said Mr Belter.
'Here's an easy one for Tony.
Tony and Tessa told us about how they found a
bottle of milk on the doorstep of the house where
Mrs Nash lives.
Tony knew that the milkman had not been
there that day.
He knew the milk had been left there the day before.
He found out that Mrs Nash was hurt.'
'Yes,' said Tessa.
'They took her to hospital on a stretcher.'
'That's right,' said Mr Belter.
'When she came out of hospital, Tony and Tessa and
their Mum and Dad played music in the park.
Tony played something that Rocky and Ben
had bought from Mrs Chant.
What did Tony play?'

'Number 16,' said Mr Belter.
'Now we don't often get leopards in Wellington Square,
but Rocky was in the newspapers when the lovely
Ramona Rome lost her pet leopard.
Rocky told us about how Ramona's leopard
came into his tent and ate something.
Can you tell me:
What did the leopard eat?'

'Number 17,' said Mr Belter.
'I don't know if you remember when
we played a football match and
someone in this class got sent off for foul play.'
'I remember that,' said Kevin.
'I remember that stupid referee sending me off and
I remember that Mr Belter had to pick me up from
the police station, because I got lost in the town and
a policeman found me sitting in a doorway.'
'Well, you mustn't do that again, Kevin,'
said Mr Belter.
'What I want to know is:
Which team were Waterloo School playing at football?'

'Number 18,' said Mr Belter.

'Mrs Valentine's house caught fire.

Do you remember all the smoke?

As well as rescuing Mrs Valentine, the fireman made
another rescue from the roof of her house.'

'I know who it was,' said Rocky. 'It was Fireman Salter.'

'No,' said Mr Belter.

'I don't want to know the name of the fireman.

I want to know who or what was rescued.

Who was rescued from the roof?'

'Number 19,' said Mr Belter.

'Do you remember when we went on our
trip to France?'

'That's when we got lost and we met that French
boy, Marc,' said Rocky.

'We got lost again at that crossroads,' said Ben.

'We could only speak English and
no-one understood us.'

Mr Belter went on,

'Once we had got off the boat in the French port,
we couldn't use the money we use in England.'

'I remember that,' said Jamila.

'I had a big brown note.'

'Yes,' said Mr Belter. 'We had to use French money.
English money is called pounds.

What is the money called in France?'

'Number 20 – the last one!' said Mr Belter.
'I bet no-one gets this one right.
When we went to France, did you notice
a car or a lorry going along the road?
Did you notice which side of the road they drove on?'
'I know,' said Rocky.
'So do I,' said Ben.
'We rode along a road on Marc's cart.'
'Well, you two should get this right,' said Mr Belter.
'What was that again?' asked Wing Chan.
Mr Belter said,
'Which side of the road do they drive on in France?'

If you want to check how much you know about
Wellington Square, you can turn to p 30 and see how
many you got right, and then turn back to p 25 to read
the rest of the book.

On the other hand, you could read the rest of the book
now and then look at p 30 to see how well you did.

The next day was the last day of term.
In the morning the class helped Mr Belter to
put away all the books and all the papers.
Then they all got the classroom ready for the party.
Everyone had brought something to eat or drink.
Some people had brought a cake and
some had brought apples.
Someone had brought sausage rolls and
someone had brought a big pork pie.
Mr Belter had brought lots of drink, jelly and ice-cream.
Kevin had brought his big radio to play very loud music.

At the end of the party, Mr Belter told everyone
to be quiet.
'I have looked through yesterday's work and I can now
tell you the names of the three people who really know
a lot about Wellington Square,' said Mr Belter.
'At number three, with 28 marks, is Ben.'
Everyone cheered.
'Second, with 34 marks, is Rocky.' Everyone cheered.
'And first, with 40 marks, is... Tessa!' Everyone cheered.
'For coming top, you get this big bag of sweets. Well
done!'

'Now, it's time to go home,' said Mr Belter.
'Have a good break and come back next term ready to
do lots of work for your next teacher.'

Tony and Tessa ran into their house.

'Tessa came top!' said Tony.

'Top of what?' said the twins' mother.

'I won this bag of sweets,' said Tessa.

'I won *What do you know about Wellington Square?*
I was the only one who got them all right!'

'What a clever girl!' said Mrs Potts.

'I got 25,' said Tony. 'I did quite well.'

'What clever twins!' said Mrs Potts.

'Wing Chan asked if we could go to his
house tomorrow,' said Tessa. 'Is that OK?'

'Yes,' said Mrs Potts.

'And he can come round here for tea one day next
week.'

Jamila went into her Dad's shop.
Mr Patel was putting bags into the
cupboard under the till.
'Have you done lots of work today?' said Mr Patel.
'We haven't done any work today,' said Jamila.
'We had our end of term party.'
'Well, you can do a little bit of work now,' said her Dad.
'I have to go out, but I will only be ten minutes.
The shop's still open.
Can you look after it for me?'

Just as Mr Patel went out,
Wing Chan came in to buy some sweets.
'What are you doing tomorrow?' asked Wing Chan.
'Nothing, really,' said Jamila. 'Why?'
'Would you like to come round to my house for tea?'
said Wing Chan. 'Tony and Tessa are coming.'
'That would be great,' said Jamila.
'I'll see my Dad about it when he's back, but
I'm sure it'll be OK.'
'We'll have something to eat, then we'll go in the park,'
said Wing Chan.
'OK,' said Jamila. 'See you tomorrow.'

Kevin walked through the back door.

'Was it a good party?' asked Kevin's mother.

'Yes, it was OK,' said Kevin, dropping
his bag on the floor, 'but I think I feel a bit ill.
There was lots to eat.
There were sausage rolls and ice-cream and jelly.'

'Oh,' said Kevin's mother.

'I didn't know you were having food at your party.
I've just made you this plate of fish and chips for tea.'
Kevin looked at the big plate of fish and chips.

'Oh,' said Kevin.

'Just for once, I don't really feel like fish and chips.
I think I might have eaten just a bit too much.'

'Kevin,' said his mother.

'Why has your face gone that funny colour?'

'I think I'm going to be very ill,' said Kevin, as he
backed out of the room and rushed upstairs.

Two minutes later, Kevin came back.

'I feel better now,' said Kevin.

'Where's that plate of fish and chips?'

Rocky and Ben walked out of the school gate.
'What shall we do tomorrow?' asked Rocky.
'You can come round to my house,' said Ben.
'We can play on my trampoline.'
'OK,' said Rocky. 'See you tomorrow.'

Rocky could hear Max's barking as
he went into his house.
Max always made a noise when
he heard Rocky's footsteps.
'Have you had a good day at school?'
asked Rocky's mother.
'Yes,' said Rocky. 'We had a great party.
It was our last day in Mr Belter's class.
It seems funny to think that we'll have
another teacher when we start next term.
I feel as if I've been in Mr Belter's class for ages, but
it's not that long ago that I started at Waterloo School.'
'Are you glad that we moved into Wellington Square?'
said Mrs Rockwell.
'Oh, yes, Mum,' said Rocky.
'I wasn't sure at first, but now I think that moving into
Wellington Square was a really good thing for us!'

The end

You get two marks for each right answer.

1 What sort of food was the fox stealing from
the fish and chip shop?
(*Rocky's fox*)
The fox was stealing **chicken**.

2 What sort of animal did Ben rescue from the canal?
(*Afraid of the water*)
Ben rescued **a kitten**.

3 There are two things Brian loves to eat. What are they?
(*What a mystery!*)
His favourite things are **bananas** and **flowers**.
(you get 1 for **bananas** and 1 for **flowers**.)

4 Who owns the shop where Tony and Tessa
bought their masks?
(*Aliens*)
Mr Miller (Kevin's Dad's brother) owns the shop.

5 Who owned the little dog?
(*Jamila at the fair*)
The fortune teller (Madame Rose) owned the little dog.

6 What did the bomb turn out to be?
(*Bomb scare*)
It turned out to be **Kevin's radio**.

7 What had killed the animals in the pond?
(*Danger in the pond*)
A man had put an old tin of **weed killer** and
other rubbish in the pond.

8 What is the name for the water which
goes all round the castle?
(*Prisoners in the dungeon*)
The water round the castle is called **a moat**.

9 What did the burglar steal from the school?
(*The radio mystery*)
The burglar took **Mr Belter's cash-box**.

10 Who called an ambulance?
(*Accident!*)
Jamila told Fred about the accident and
Fred called an ambulance.

11 What object did Mr March give Ben?
(*Going for gold*)
Mr March gave Ben **a gold medal**.

12 Who got Rocky and the kite down from the tree?
(*The dragon kite*)
WPC Clark climbed up a ladder and
got Rocky and the kite down.

13 What was Fred's Grandad's work in the war?
(*Bombs over Wellington Square*)
Fred's Grandad was **an air raid warden**.

14 What did Fred give Rocky to remember
the day he found a bomb?
(*Bombs over Wellington Square*)
Fred gave Rocky **his Grandad's tin hat**.

15 What did Tony play?
(*The Good Samaritans*)
Tony and his Mum both played **the guitar**.

16 What did the leopard eat?
(*Safari park*)
The leopard ate **Rocky's pork pie**.

17 Which team were Waterloo School playing at football?
(*Playing away*)
Waterloo School were playing **Ripton Rovers**.

18 Who was rescued from the roof?
(*Rescue service*)
Fireman Salter rescued **Sing-Sing**, Mrs Valentine's
cat, from the roof. Cats are always having accidents!

19 What is the money called in France?
(*Hello France!*)
French money is called **francs**.

20 Which side of the road do they drive on in France?
(*Hello France!*)
Both - just as they do in any other country!

That was Mr Belter being funny!
You can have three marks if you said **both**, but
you can have two marks if you said that they
drive on the **right**.